Marie Berrondo-

MATHS À LA CARTE

for Years 5 and 6

BEAM

ACKNOWLEDGEMENTS

Special thanks to Roberta Faulhaber-Razafy for translating this book into English.

Helen Elis Jones, University of Wales, Bangor

Carolyn Wallis, St Nicholas House Junior School, Hertfordshire

C Wallis, Abbot's Hill Junior School, Hertfordshire

Joyce Atkinson, Croham Hurst Junior School, Croydon

Karen Cooke, Sunnymede Junior School, Essex

Carrie Higson, Abermule Community Primary School, Powys

Suzanne Hamilton, Glyncollen Primary School, Swansea

Andrea Trigg and V Pearce, Felbridge Primary School, West Sussex

Gaynor Dalrympole, Meadow Vale Primary School, Bracknell Forest

Judith Dodds, Owlsmoor Primary School, Bracknell Forest

Hilary Osborn and Lesley Chambers, Cranford House School, Oxfordshire

Lyn Wickham, Lissa Schmolz and Hayley Frampton, Bidbury Junior School, Hampshire

Kath John, Associate Adviser for Numeracy, School Improvement Service, Glamorgan

Sian Davies, Y Bont Faen Primary School, Glamorgan

Sarah Burgess, St Wulston's & St Edmund's Catholic Primary School, Lancashire

Jenni Ewan, Preston Lodge High School, East Lothian

Kate Paige, Numeracy Consultant, Middlesbrough

Jackie Ross, Kincardineshire

Cathy Bennett, Ridgeway Primary School, Sheffield

Heidi Williams and Cranbourne Primary School, Berkshire

Sue Potts, Harmans Water Primary School, Bracknell Forest

Catherine Graham and Skelton Primary School, Cleveland

Carol Payton and Bentley Drive JMI School, Walsall

Alison Williams, Gors Community School, Swansea

David Lewis and Anthony Corkes, St Joseph's Primary School, Swansea

Sharon Sutton, Institute of Education, University of Reading

Fr Rudolf Loewenstein, St Christina's School, London

Published by BEAM Education

Maze Workshops

72a Southgate Road

London N1 3JT

Telephone 020 77684 3323

Fax 020 7684 3334

Email info@beam.co.uk

© Beam Education 2007, a division of Nelson Thornes
ISBN 978 1 9031 4298 1

British Library Cataloguing-in-Publication Data

Data available

Edited by Marion Dill

Designed by Malena Wilson-Max

Illustrations by Adrienne Salgado

Printed in Hong Kong

CONTENTS

3

HOW TO USE THE CD-ROM

You'll find the following on the *Maths à la Carte Years 5 and 6* CD-ROM:

• 99 problems

• a map of Paris

• five English-French files:

  Colours

  Days of the week

  Greetings

  Family

  Numbers

You can either project the individual problem pages onto a whiteboard from your computer or print them out onto acetate sheets and use them on an overhead projector.

The simple map of Paris will give children an idea where some of the sights mentioned in the book are, and the English-French files are a great way to introduce some basic French to young mathematicians and budding linguists.

Bonjour!

Here are 99 challenging maths problems and puzzles for maths lessons with a difference!

I invented these maths problems in France. Why? Because I'm French! And when I was about your age, I discovered that maths can be amusing, exciting and great fun.

Later in life, I taught maths at university for many years. What I liked most, though, was explaining maths and the magical world of numbers to my four children and then my three grandchildren. Thanks to those seven people, I have written this book, which is serious and, at the same time, not serious at all …

Marie Berrondo-Agrell

BON APPÉTIT TO THE LIONS

If 4 lions eat 4 gazelles in 4 days, how many gazelles will 2 lions eat in 2 days?

Over to you!

Topsy-turvy tip

How many gazelles will 4 lions eat in 2 days?

CHRISTMAS LOG

Maman needs 2 seconds to cut the Christmas log in two. To cut it into 5 slices, she needs 5 seconds, right?

Over to you!

Topsy-turvy tip

How many cuts do you need to cut the log into 5 slices?

HOW OLD IS GRAND-PÈRE?

Maman is 38, and Papa is 5 years older. I am 2 years younger than Papa. Grand-Père is 31 years older than Maman, and Grand-Mère is 2 years younger than Grand-Père. How old is Grand-Père?

Over to you!

L'ÂGE DE GRAND-PÈRE

Maman a 38 ans. Papa a 5 ans de plus. J'ai 2 ans de moins que Papa. Grand-Père a 31 ans de plus que Maman. Et Grand-Mère a 2 ans de moins que Grand-Père. Quel âge a Grand-Père?

C'est à toi!

FAST FOOD

If I order two hamburgers, two portions of chips and an orange juice, I pay € 9. If I order one hamburger and one portion of chips, I pay € 4. How much does an orange juice cost?

Over to you!

Topsy-turvy tip

How much do two hamburgers and two portions of chips cost?

MAMAN, MY TWIN SISTER AND ME

Maman is 37. Last year, she was four times older than me. How old is my twin sister today?

Over to you!

Topsy-turvy tip

How old was Maman last year?

MÉTRO OPÉRA

There are 57 people on my underground train. We just stopped at the Opéra station. Nine people got off, and 13 got on. How many people were on the train before we stopped at Opéra?

Over to you!

Topsy-turvy tip

How many would be there if no one had got on the train?

A FRAGRANT DINNER

"I would like 3 cauliflowers at € 2 apiece, 15 cm of garlic sausage at 15 cent per centimetre, half of an old Camembert cheese at € 5 each, a kilogram of turnips at € 1 per half-kilo and a jar of that *bouillabaisse*, delicious fish soup, at € 6."

I have € 20 in my purse. I would like to buy some mint chewing gum to freshen my breath. Do I have any money left over to do so?

Over to you!

Topsy-turvy tip

How much did my shopping cost?

TARZAN IN HONOLULU

It's 6:30 pm. I have just turned off the TV. I turned it on at 5:19 pm to watch a film called *Tarzan in Honolulu*. Tarzan's wife, Jane, was wearing a leopard-spotted swimming suit, and Tarzan screamed every 7 minutes. The film finished with one last shriek. How many times did Tarzan scream during the film?

Over to you!

Topsy-turvy tip

How long did the film last?

ABDULLAH IN THE DESERT

Abdullah is walking in the middle of the desert with his Bactrian camels and dromedaries. Together they have a total of 34 feet and 13 humps. Does Abdullah have more dromedaries than camels or more camels than dromedaries?

Over to you!

Topsy-turvy tip

Abdullah has two feet. Bactrian camels have two humps, dromedaries one hump.

ABDULLAH DANS LE DÉSERT

Abdullah se promène au milieu du désert avec ses chameaux Bactrian et ses dromadaires. Cela fait en tout 34 pieds et 13 bosses. Abdullah a-t-il ainsi plus de dromadaires que de chameaux ou plus de chameaux que de dromadaires?

C'est à toi!

QUICHE LORRAINE

You are making a quiche lorraine in a flat, round pan with a 16 cm radius. The recipe includes flour, butter, bacon, eggs and cream. Your kitchen oven is 35 cm wide, 31 cm deep and 33 cm high. How are you going to put the dish in the oven without burning yourself?

Over to you!

Topsy-turvy tip

What is the diameter of the quiche?

ADORABLE TRIANGLES

Monsieur and Madame Triangle have 5 children. Here they are, but their names are all mixed up. Please put them back where they belong.

Over to you!

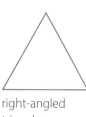  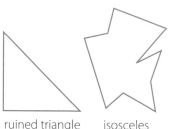 

right-angled triangle   equilateral triangle   ruined triangle   isosceles triangle   right-angled isosceles triangle

Topsy-turvy tip

Review what you know about triangles.

AT THE BAKER'S

When you buy 2 croissants and 4 pains au chocolat, it costs € 5,40.
What do 3 croissants and 6 pains au chocolat cost?

Over to you!

Topsy-turvy tip

How much do
1 croissant and
2 pains au chocolat cost?

À LA BOULANGÉRIE

Quand tu achètes 2 croissants et 4 pains au chocolat, cela te coûte
€ 5,40. Combien dois-tu alors payer pour 3 croissants et 6 pains
au chocolat?

C'est à toi!

WAGADA KOKONIMOON

Here you are on Kokonimoon Island. You catch a 53 decagram octopus, 11 small crabs weighing 1272 decigrams each and a 4.07 kg sea tortoise. Will this be enough supper for Wagada, your tame bear cub, who needs to eat 6 kg of food every evening?

Over to you!

Topsy-turvy tip

Watch out:
1 decagram = 10 grams
1 decigram = one tenth of a gram

TEN KILOMETRES OF HAIR

I am the giant Gargantua. In total, my hair is 10 kilometres long. Each hair is exactly 4 cm long. How many hairs do I have on my head?

Over to you!

Topsy-turvy tip

How many metres of hair do I have?

WITH PAUL AT CHIWAKATEPEC

It's 7 o'clock in the morning. We are about to climb Chiwakatepec which is 600 metres high. We all climb 100 metres per hour except for Paul, who climbs 2 metres per minute. When we all reach the top, we'll have a picnic. At what time will we eat?

Over to you!

Topsy-turvy tip

How long did the group take?
How long did Paul take?

CHOCOLATES FOR EASTER

If 3 chocolate hens and 2 chocolate bells cost € 9,40 and
4 chocolate hens and 3 chocolate bells cost € 13,10,
how much will 1 chocolate hen and 1 chocolate bell cost?

Over to you!

Topsy-turvy tip

Pay attention to the
difference between
the first two purchases.

UP THE EIFFEL TOWER

We are climbing up to the 1st floor of the Eiffel Tower. It is more fun
and less expensive than taking the lift, even if it is kind of scary. So,
right now Marion is 9 metres above me, Violette 6 metres below
Lucile, Lucile is 4 metres higher than Emilie, and Emilie is 5 metres
below Marion. The last one up will treat the four others to chocolate
ice cream. Who will be the lucky girl?

Over to you!

Topsy-turvy tip

Draw a vertical line and
locate the five girls.

MAMAN IS A MATHS TEACHER

Maman is a maths teacher. She is correcting her tests, and has
two left to do. But suddenly she has a terrible headache, and
I have to correct the tests for her:

Adrien Dupont			
25	739	1524	1989
× 4	+ 8428	− 1239	+ 1989
100	9157	1285	3898

Anne-Sophie Dubois			
25	739	1524	1989
× 4	+ 8428	− 1239	+ 1989
250	9167	315	3978

Who gets the worst mark?

Over to you!

Topsy-turvy tip

Begin by doing the four
problems yourself.

MATHS TEST

It was a horribly difficult maths test. I handed in my paper in tears
after 52 minutes and 77 seconds. My best friend, Violette, collapsed
after 3213 seconds. My friend Pierre-Alexandre lasted 1 hour minus
7 minutes. Which of the three of us handed in their test first?

Over to you!

Topsy-turvy tip

Write all the times
in minutes or seconds.

A MYSTERY

I am a number with two different figures. I have 8 more units than the tens. Who am I?

Over to you!

Topsy-turvy tip

Don't forget that the tens digit is at least 1, and that the units digit is at most 9.

300 METRES OF EIFFEL TOWER

Gustave Eiffel was born on 15 December 1832. The first shovelfuls of earth for the Eiffel Tower's foundations were removed when he was 54 years and one and a half months old. The inauguration was held when the tower reached its final height of 300 metres on Sunday, 31 March 1889. How many months did it take to build the Eiffel Tower?

Over to you!

Topsy-turvy tip

When did construction begin?

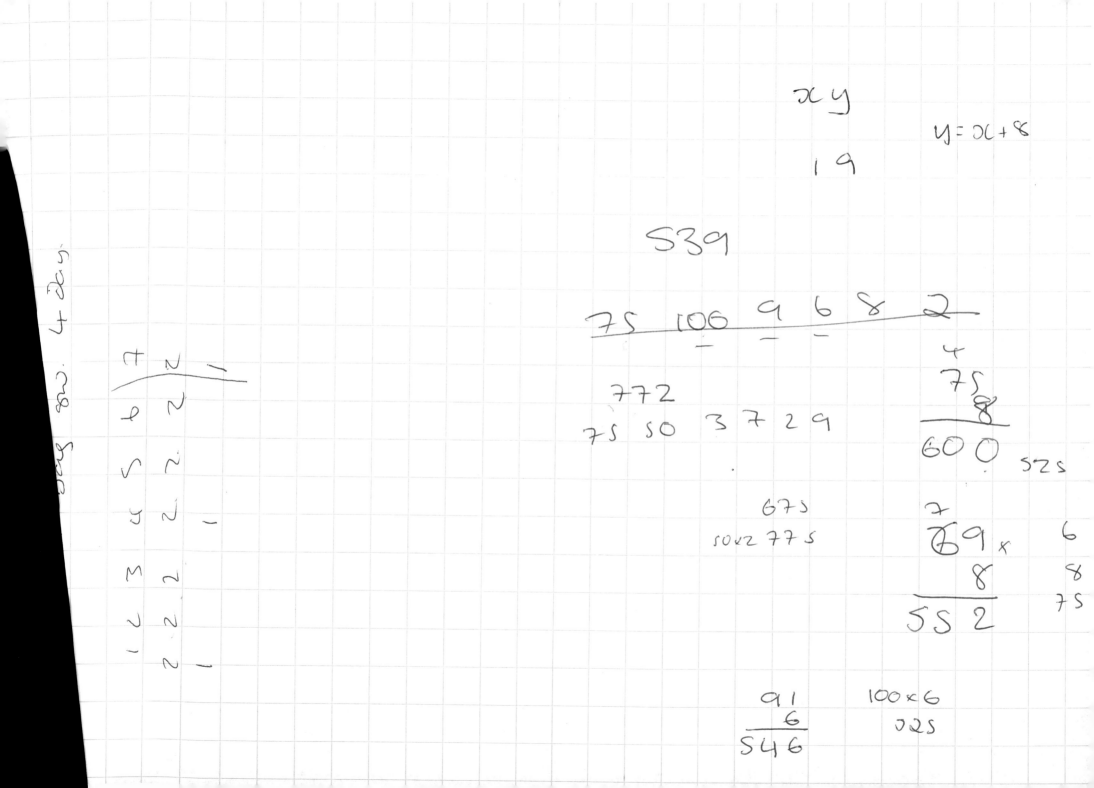

BAKED EGGS

The big fat hen lays 2 eggs a day. The little skinny hen lays 1 egg every three days. How many days do they need to fill a round box of 14 eggs?

Over to you!

Topsy-turvy tip

How many eggs can you collect in three days?

SEVEN CRAZY ARROWS

In my maths notebook there were seven sensible arrows that pointed to the name of each shape. Suddenly, they went completely crazy. Here is the result:

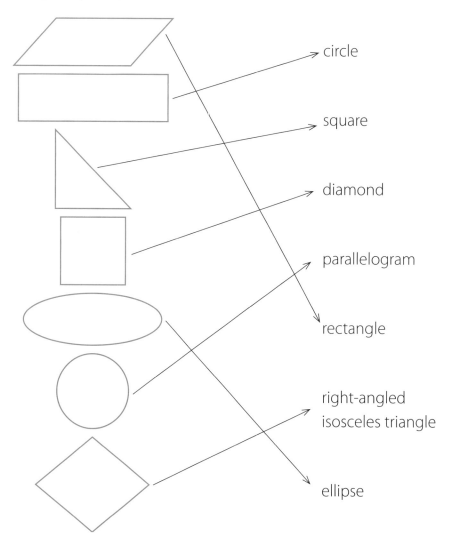

Which arrow has not lost its mind?

Over to you!

SEPT FLÈCHES FOLLES

Dans mon cahiers de mathématiques, il y avait 7 flèches tout à fait raisonnables qui marquaient le nom de chaque figure géométrique. Soudainement, elles sont devenues complètement folles, et voici le résultat:

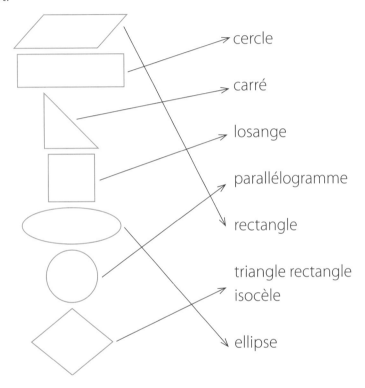

cercle

carré

losange

parallélogramme

rectangle

triangle rectangle isocèle

ellipse

Quelle est la seule flèche qui est restée raisonnable? C'est à toi!

A KHAKI ANORAK

Maman has just bought me the khaki anorak of my dreams for € 40. It was in a sale with a 50% discount. How much did it cost before the sale?

Over to you!

Topsy-turvy tip

If you subtract half of the price, half is left.

ANOTHER SEVEN CRAZY ARROWS

Would you believe, in my maths notebook, there were another seven sensible arrows which suddenly went completely crazy. Here is the result:

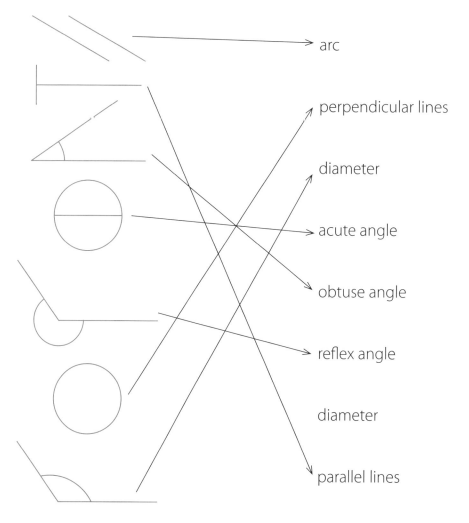

Which arrow is still sane?

Over to you!

Topsy-turvy tip

Use a good maths dictionary.

TAKE CARE OF YOUR TEETH

Let's say, 4 children eat 4 bags of sweets in 4 days. Imagine how many days it will take 10 children to eat 10 bags of sweets.

Over to you!

Topsy-turvy tip

How much does one child eat in 4 days?

MIRROR, MIRROR ...

Here I am looking out of the mirror:

As you can see, my right ear sticks out, there's a spot of ink on my left cheek, and my mouth is crooked, but apart from that, I am really cute. Can you tell me the number of stripes on my turtleneck sweater?

Over to you!

Topsy-turvy tip

Look at yourself in a mirror.

THE LITTLE WATER LILY AND THE BIG CASTLE

Once upon a time, a very lovely water lily lived in a small pond outside a big castle. The lily doubled its area every day. After 20 days, the entire pond was white.

Can you tell me how many days it took for the water lily to cover a quarter of the little pond?

Over to you!

Topsy-turvy tip

What is happening
on day 19?

PARIS-LONDON-HELSINKI

When it is noon in Paris, it is 11 am in London and 1 pm in Helsinki.
It is now 12:30 pm in London. What time is it in Helsinki?

Over to you!

Topsy-turvy tip

How many hours are there
between London and
Helsinki?

SMALL TOYS

I love to collect toy figures. Napoléon on horseback costs € 2
more than a Roman soldier. A cowboy costs € 1. A farmer costs
€ 3 more than a Gaul. A Gaul costs as much as a Roman soldier.
A Martian costs € 7. A farmer costs as much as 5 cowboys.
How much does the Napoléon on horseback cost?

Over to you!

Topsy-turvy tip

To what can you compare
the price of the Napoléon?

SUDOKULOGIC

Below is a table full of 0s and 1s, with one 1 per line and per column:

			Total
0	1	0	1
1	0	0	1
0	0	1	1
Total			
1	1	1	

Draw out the table below and fill it in the same way.

			Total
0			1
			1
0		0	1
Total			
1	1	1	

Over to you!

EVERYTHING EVERYWHERE

Sometimes I sleep at Maman's and sometimes at Papa's. Sometimes I sleep at Grand-Mère and Grand-Père's house. Now I am at school. I have forgotten my pencil case, my sports kit and my maths notebook. I know I forgot one thing at each house.

The maths notebook can't be at Maman's. The pencil case can't be with Grand-Mère and Grand-Père. I know Maman doesn't have the pencil case either. Where did I forget my maths notebook?

Over to you!

	Maman	Papa	Grand-Mère/Grand-Père
maths notebook			
sports kit			
pencil case			

Topsy-turvy tip

Use a sudoku-logic table.

MOTHER'S DAY

In France, 1 rose costs € 1, the same as 2 tulips or 3 marguerites. Will my € 5 be enough to buy 3 roses, 3 tulips and 3 marguerites as a present for Maman on Mother's Day?

Over to you!

Topsy-turvy tip

How much would 3 roses, 2 tulips and 3 marguerites cost?

PARIS-BIARRITZ

We are travelling from Paris to Biarritz by car. That is a distance of nearly 800 km.

The car burns 6 litres every 100 kilometres. One litre of petrol costs € 1,20. The petrol tank contains 42 litres. Papa filled up the tank before we left, and he has about € 50 left in his wallet. Do we need to stop on the road to fill her up?

Over to you!

Topsy-turvy tip

Watch out for useless information!

IN THE BELLY OF THE WHALE

Jonah was lost in the whale's belly, 4 metres down the whale's throat. But he succeeded in sliding forward two thirds of a metre every hour. When he reached the mouth, the whale spat him out. *Oof*! How many slimey hours did Jonah spend inside the whale?

Over to you!

Topsy-turvy tip

How far did Jonah move in two hours?

THE SNAIL AND THE TORTOISE

Once upon a time, there was a tortoise who waddled 3 metres in every 3 hours and a snail who slid 22 cm in 11 minutes. They ran a race. Which animal won?

Over to you!

Topsy-turvy tip

Work out how far they travel in one minute.

GOING TO SCHOOL

On my way to school, I have to pass by …

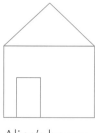

Alice's house

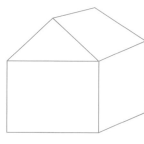

Colombe's house

and Jeanne's house

Which house can you draw without lifting the pencil from the paper?

Over to you!

Topsy-turvy tip

As you draw, you go across intersections, some connecting an even number of lines and some an odd number. Watch out: these could stop you.

HOW OLD IS PAPA?

When Papa was 8, Grand-Père was 39. Today, Grand-Père is twice as old as Papa. How old is Papa?

Over to you!

Topsy-turvy tip

What is the difference in their ages?

FROM MARSEILLES TO NEWCASTLE

Here is a crowded car ferry going from Marseilles to Newcastle.
It does not take foot passengers. In the car-parking zone, there
are 360 cars. Half of them had 3 people in them, and the rest
had 2 people in them. Are there enough beds on the ferry
for everybody?

Over to you!

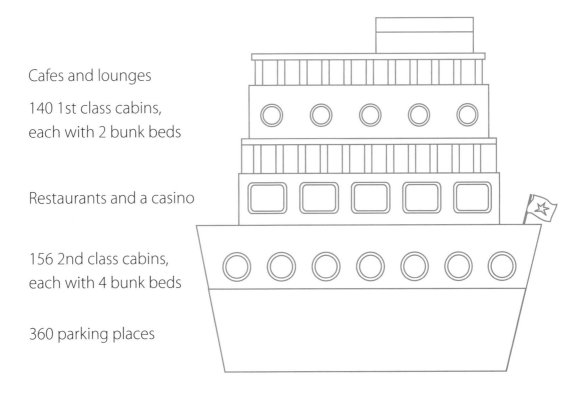

Cafes and lounges

140 1st class cabins,
each with 2 bunk beds

Restaurants and a casino

156 2nd class cabins,
each with 4 bunk beds

360 parking places

Topsy-turvy tip

Count the number of
bunk beds.

FRENCH HISTORY

Louis XVIII reigned from 1815 to 1824. Charles X then reigned three years less than Louis XVIII. After that, Louis-Philippe was king 3 times longer than Charles X. Then the République was founded that lasted 14 years less than the reign of Louis-Philippe. Can you say what year Napoléon III was finally elected Emperor of France just after this République?

Over to you!

ANATOLE AND ZOÉ

Anatole says: "I have as many brothers as sisters." Zoé says: "I have twice as many brothers as sisters." How many children are there in Anatole and Zoé's family?

Over to you!

MINIATURE CARS

I own a Peugeot, a Citroën and a Renault. One is black, one is grey, and the last one is red. The Peugeot is not black, and the Citroën is not red. If my red car is not the Peugeot, what colour is my Citroën?

Over to you!

Topsy-turvy tip

Try to use sudoku logic (see p26).

AUTOS MINIATURES

J'ai une Peugeot, une Citroën et une Renault. L'une est noire, l'autre est grise, et la dernière est rouge. Ma Peugeot n'est pas noire. Ma Citroën n'est pas rouge. Si ma voiture rouge n'est pas la Peugeot, de quelle couleur est ma Citroën?

C'est à toi!

AERIAL VIEWS

Seen from a helicopter, Maman's house is a square with 7 metre long sides. Seen from a helicopter, Papa's house, where I go on weekends, is a 4 x 12 metre rectangle. I have to spend Christmas with the parent whose house has the longest perimeter and Easter with the one whose house has the biggest area.

With whom do I spend Christmas and with whom Easter?

Over to you!

FISH WITH RASPBERRIES

Maman goes shopping. She takes a special bag to keep the food cold. The bag holds 10 packets. She has two € 20 in her purse. She buys 3 packets of fish for € 2,50 each, 2 guinea fowl for € 6 each, 4 packets of freshly made soup for € 3,50 each and a brioche for € 1,50. Is it sensible also to buy a punnet of raspberries for € 5?

Over to you!

POLYTECHNICIANS' PARADE

It's July 14th, and I'm off to see the big parade on the Champs
Elysées in Paris. All the students from Polytechnique Université
are carefully lined up in lines and columns, wearing their parade
uniforms. I can see my big brother who is a student at the
Polytechnique. He has two friends to his left, 17 to his right,
21 in a straight line in front and 8 right behind him.

How many students go to the famous Polytechnique?

Over to you!

Topsy-turvy tip

Calculate the number of
polytechnicians by line
and column.

35

THE DELAROCHE-DUPLESSIS FAMILY

The Delaroche-Duplessis' have 5 children. Each child is older or younger than the others by exactly 2 years, so that on the day of their next group birthday, they will need 5 cakes with 35 candles in all. How many candles will Augustin-Charles, the eldest, need on his cake?

Over to you!

Topsy-turvy tip

What ages would they all be if the youngest were 1?

EVERYBODY INTO THE CAR

Papa (85 kilograms), Maman (65 kilograms), my little sister (18 kilograms), my elder brother (42 kilograms), the suitcases (27 kilograms) and, of course, myself are going on holiday in our car. We are leaving our little dog (7 kilograms) and our large cat (5 kilograms) with the neighbours. If our car weighs 1323 kilograms when it is empty and 1587 kilograms when it is full, how much do I weigh?

Over to you!

Topsy-turvy tip

Watch out for useless information!

AN ELEPHANT FOR THE WHOLE CLASS

There are 28 students in our class. A quarter of them are girls, and each girl weighs an average of 33 kilos, 3 kilos more than each boy. If Robrouf, the elephant, weighs 1000 kilos, who weighs the most: Robrouf or all the students in the class together?

Over to you!

Topsy-turvy tip

How much would the students weigh if they were all girls?

AT THE CHÂTEAU DE SAILLESVER

One pound was worth 11 francs at the end of the last century. Then, a ticket to visit the Château de Saillesver cost 33 francs. Today, one pound is worth € 1, 50, and a ticket to Saillesver costs € 3. Is it more or less expensive for an English tourist to visit the Château today?

Over to you!

Topsy-turvy tip

Compare the two prices in pounds.

PARIS BLUES

Here we are in Paris, gazing at the beautiful River Seine from a *bateau-mouche*, a very nice, open boat, while listening to a trio playing classical jazz. The players are Django Lejeune, Charlie Petit and Joe Tatin. We can hear a trumpet, percussion and a piano. We know that Django Lejeune does not play percussion, the pianist is not Django Lejeune and the percussionist is not Charlie Petit. Who plays the piano?

Over to you!

Topsy-turvy tip

Try to use sudokulogic (see p26).

FROM 1 TO 99

When you write the numbers from 1 to 99, which digit do you use the least?

Over to you!

Topsy-turvy tip

Think about the digits
in the tens place.

I LOVE EURO DISNEY!

I am just leaving Euro Disney, where I visited the Pirate Boat, the Ghost Mansion and the Magic Mountain. It was terrifying! One of the attractions gave me a headache, another one made me nauseous, and yet another one gave me nightmares. But the Magic Mountain did not give me a headache or make me feel sick, and the Pirate Ship did not give me nightmares. Oh, and the Pirate Ship didn't give me a headache either. Which one gave me nightmares?

Over to you!

	nausea	nightmares	headache
Pirate Ship			
Ghost Mansion			
Magic Mountain			

Topsy-turvy tip

Try to use sudokulogic
(see p26).

WATERLOO STATION

Did you know that Napoléon lost the battle of Waterloo against England and its allies on 18 June 1815? Then, 33 years later, the name Waterloo was given to a large railway station in London. In which year will we celebrate the 150th birthday of Waterloo Station?

Over to you!

Topsy turvy tip

How much is 48 + 1509?

THE DUBOIS FAMILY

The Dubois' have six children. Each child is older or younger than the others by exactly 3 years. When they have their joint birthday, they all share one very large, scrumptious cake with candles for each child. Last year, Marie, the youngest, was 5. Will two packs of 40 candles be enough for this year's cake?

Over to you!

Topsy-turvy tip

What age will Marie be this year?

ALEXANDRINE IN PARIS

Alexandrine is visiting Paris. Today, she plans to go to the Île de la Cité and the Île Saint-Louis to see the charming little streets and bridges.

Alexandrine wants to cross each bridge only once. What route should she take?

Over to you!

MY GREAT-GRANDMOTHER'S 100TH BIRTHDAY

My great-grandmother received a baby tortoise as a birthday present when she was 3. The tortoise died at the ripe old age of 93. That happened two years ago on my 9th birthday. In how many years will we celebrate my great-grandmother's 100th birthday?

Over to you!

Topsy-turvy tip

How old was my great-grandmother two years ago?

FEEDING THE GIRAFFES

If you keep giraffes, you feed them by hanging boxes of fragrant hay in trees. One giraffe eats 3 boxes in two days. So how many boxes do you need to feed 2 giraffes for 3 days?

Over to you!

Topsy-turvy tip

2 giraffes in 1 day eat as much as 1 giraffe eats in 2 days.

STEAK FRITES FOR MARGUERITE

My little sister Marguerite has the following number of teeth:

$$\frac{20}{4} + \frac{8}{2} - \frac{15}{5} + \frac{6}{3} - \frac{7}{7}$$

Can she eat steak and chips?

Over to you!

UN STEAK FRITES POUR MARGUERITE

Voici le nombre de dents de ma petite sœur Marguerite:

$$\frac{20}{4} + \frac{8}{2} - \frac{15}{5} + \frac{6}{3} - \frac{7}{7}$$

Peut-elle manger un steak frites?

C'est à toi!

THE TRUE STORY OF NOAH'S ARK

When the deluge began, Noah put pairs of all the animal species he could find into his boat. When the water went down again, you could see large mountains. Noah unloaded half of his animal pairs in Africa on Kilimanjaro. Later, he unloaded half of those remaining in Asia on Mount Everest. The final 13 animal pairs were unloaded in South America on Popocatepetl.

How many animals did Noah save?

Over to you!

Topsy-turvy tip

How many animals were unloaded onto Mount Everest?

AUSTERLITZ STATION

Did you know that Napoléon won a brilliant victory against Austria and Russia at the battle of Austerlitz on 2 December 1802? Then, 63 years later, a big railway station in Paris was named Austerlitz after that battle. In what year will the French celebrate the 150th anniversary of the Austerlitz railway station?

Over to you!

Topsy-turvy tip

How much is 63 + 1509?

TRAVELLING

My yellow suitcase weighs 3 kilos less than my blue suitcase.
My green suitcase weighs 3 kilos more than my yellow suitcase.
All three suitcases weigh 27 kilos. How much does my yellow
suitcase weigh?

Over to you!

Topsy-turvy tip

What would all three
suitcases weigh if
the yellow suitcase
were 3 kilos heavier?

EN VOYAGE

Ma valise jaune pèse 3 kilos de moins que ma valise bleue.
Ma valise verte pèse 3 kilos de plus que ma valise jaune. Mes
3 valises ensemble pèsent 27 kilos. Combien pèse ma valise jaune?

C'est à toi!

PAPAYAS AND KIWIS

When you buy 3 papayas, 1 mango and 2 kiwis, it costs € 9,25.
When you buy 2 papayas and 1 kiwi, it only costs € 5,50. How much
will you pay when you buy 1 papaya, 1 mango and 1 kiwi?

Over to you!

Topsy-turvy tip

What is the difference
between the two purchases?

DES PAPAYES ET DES KIWIS

Quand tu achètes 3 papayes, 1 mangue et 2 kiwis, cela coûte € 9,25.
Et quand tu achètes 2 papayes et 1 kiwi, cela n'en coûte que € 5,50.
Combien devras-tu payer si tu achètes 1 papaye, 1 mangue
et 1 kiwi?

C'est à toi!

ANNA, PHOEBE AND HARRIET GO TO PARIS

Anna, Phoebe and Harriet go to Paris. After paying for the hotel, they have £50 pounds left. One pound is worth € 1,50. They want to see the Eiffel Tower, where each ticket costs € 7,50, the Petit Palais, which is free, the Arc de Triomphe, where each ticket costs € 5, and the Louvre Museum, where each ticket costs € 9,50. How much money do the girls have left to pay for the Métro and a meal at a restaurant?

Over to you!

Topsy-turvy tip

How many euros in 50 pounds?

SUDOKUSTATISTICS

Below is a table showing different numbers. We have written their sums in each line or column as follows:

			Total
12	24	7	43
5	13	5	23
8	0	25	33
Total 25	37	37	99

Complete the table below by successive subtractions (that is what we call 'sudokustatistics').

		Total
		13
6		8
	3	0
Total	16	27

Over to you!

JUDO FOR GIRLS AND DANCING FOR BOYS

There are 27 children in our class, of whom 16 are girls. On Wednesday, 13 children have classical dance, 8 have judo, and the others have swimming lessons. There are 6 boys in the judo class and 3 girls in the swimming class. Are there more girls in the judo class than boys in the classical dance class?

Over to you!

Topsy-turvy tip

Try to use sudokostatistics (see p48).

	Girls	Boys	Total
Dance			
Judo			
Swimming			
Total			

PRINCESS KARAMAKAKIZOFF

My name is Princess Karamakakizoff. I am very old, and my husband is even older. I have 3 daughters and 3 son-in-laws, and each couple has 3 children. All 3 children are also married, and each couple has 3 children. Everyone is in excellent health, no one has divorced, and I am going to celebrate my 99th birthday with everybody in a restaurant with 77 seats. Do you think I have room to invite all my great-grandchildren's fiancés?

Over to you!

Topsy-turvy tip

Count the number of people in each generation carefully.

MADELEINES

Today is my birthday, and I have invited my friends to celebrate. Maman made us 50 extremely tasty madeleines, all sitting nicely in a square box. Alice, who is never hungry, only eats 1. Brigitte eats 3. Julien eats 5. Jeanne, who tends to be greedy, eats 7. Paul, who is a real glutton, eats 9. And I adore them, so I eat 11. There are still 13 left in the square box. Do you know how many madeleines were along each side of the box?

Over to you!

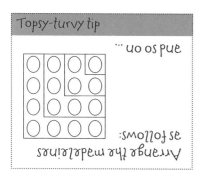

Topsy-turvy tip

Arrange the madeleines as follows:

and so on ...

COMPUTER GAMES

I have 13 vehicles, 4 of which are amphibian, so they can be used on land or in water. Five vehicles are beige, and the others are dark green. Three of my amphibian vehicles are green. How many beige vehicles do I have that I cannot use in the water?

Over to you!

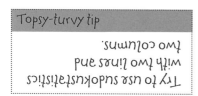

Topsy-turvy tip

Try to use sudokustatistics with two lines and two columns.

MOBILE PHONES

There are 21 students in our class, and 17 do not have a mobile phone. There are twice as many girls in the class as boys. If you know that 3 girls have a mobile phone, can you say how many boys do not have one?

Over to you!

Topsy-turvy tip

Try to use sudoku-statistics with two lines and two columns.

TÉLÉPHONES PORTABLES

Dans nôtre classe, il y a 21 élèves, dont 17 qui n'ont pas de téléphone portable. Il y a 2 fois plus de filles que de garçons. Si l'on vous dit que 3 filles ont un téléphone portable, saurez-vous dire alors combien de garçons n'en ont pas?

C'est à toi!

LONG LIVE THE CONCORDE!

During the 20th century, I liked to use the supersonic Concorde jet to go and spend a day in New York. It was really easy: I would leave Paris at 10:30 am and arrive three and a half hours later in New York, where it was only 8 o'clock in the morning. In the evening, I would leave New York at 10 pm, and the plane would land in Paris just in time for me to go directly to my apartment right next to the airport.

What time did the plane land?

Over to you!

ORANGES AND FRIENDS

There are seven of us, and we have 28 oranges to share. Everyone wants an odd number of oranges. What a dilemma!

Over to you!

WHEN JULIETTE TURNS 15 ...

Salut! I'm Juliette. Today, I am twice as old as my brother Clément, who is twice as old as my brother Baptiste, who is twice as old as my youngest brother Sylvain (measured in whole years, not months). How long will I have to wait until the age of 15, my dream age?

Over to you!

Topsy-turvy tip

Imagine that Sylvain is 2 years old.

QUENTIN, MARJOLAINE AND COMPANY

When Quentin and Marjolaine got married, both already had several children from earlier marriages. After a number of years, they ended up with 9 children at home. Quentin is the father of 5 children, and Marjolaine is the mother of 7. How many children did they have together?

Over to you!

	Quentin's children	Another father's children	Total
Marjolaine's children	1		7
Another mother's children		0	2
Total		4	9

Topsy-turvy tip

Try to use sudokustatistics with two lines and two columns.

FRUIT SALAD

Five lemons and one grapefruit weigh as much as 12 kiwis. Five kiwis and two lemons weigh as much as one grapefruit. Does a lemon weigh more or less than a kiwi?

Over to you!

Topsy-turvy tip

Get rid of the grapefruit ...

DEAR DIAGONALS

I am a polygon with 14 diagonals. How many sides do I have?

Over to you!

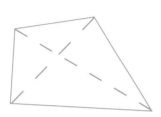

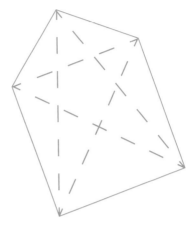

Topsy-turvy tip

A quadrilateral has 2 diagonals. How many diagonals does a pentagon have – that is, a polygon with 5 sides?

CHÈRES DIAGONALES

Je suis un polygone. J'ai 14 diagonales. Combien ai-je de côtés?

C'est à toi!

AT THE PIZZERIA

Charles ordered a pizza Marinara, but left half less one-third. Robert ordered a pizza Napolitana, but left three-fifths minus half. Yves ordered a simple Margherita, but left half minus two-eighths.
Who has the best appetite?

Over to you!

Topsy-turvy tip

How much did each one not eat?

BIG BALL

To wrap up a large ball 40 cm in diameter, you take a cube-shaped box that is just the right size and wrap it twice in a gold ribbon 4 metres long. How much is left to tie a bow?

Over to you!

Topsy-turvy tip

How many centimetres in a metre?

GRAND-MÈRE'S JUST FINE

Grand-Mère's just fine, thanks. She even still has her horrible talent for fractions. When we ask how old she is, she'll say:

"I'm three hundred and thirteen seventeenths, plus six hundred and sixty-three twenty-thirds, plus seven hundred and fifty-eight seventeenths, plus two hundred and eleven twenty-thirds."

How old is Grand-Mère?

Over to you!

Topsy-turvy tip

Add up all the 17ths, then all the 23rds.

MARTIAN TOES

It was 4 o'clock in the morning. Suddenly, I heard a loud noise in the garden. Lo and behold, there was a flying saucer landing on the lawn, and 17 cute and friendly Martians came out. I was able to get close to them and see the number of fingers they had on each of their three hands:

$$\frac{3}{7} + \frac{11}{4} + \frac{11}{7} + \frac{13}{4}$$

I also saw the number of toes they had on each of their 7 feet:

$$\frac{3}{7} + \frac{5}{4} + \frac{5}{7} + \frac{7}{4}$$

Do they have more toes than fingers or more fingers than toes?

Over to you!

> **Topsy-turvy tip**
>
> Add up all the 7ths, then all the quarters.

ABC

I am an isosceles triangle, ABC. My A angle is 50°. If my B angle is neither 50° nor 80°, how many degrees does it have?

Over to you!

> **Topsy-turvy tip**
>
> Suppose angle A is a twin with another angle the same size.

GETTING TO SCHOOL ON TIME

You live 3 kilometres from school, and you go to school by bicycle every day. The road goes uphill for 1 km, and you go slowly at 5 km per hour. The road is flat for 1 km, and you manage 15 km per hour. The road goes downhill for 1 km, and you speed up to 20 km per hour. You leave home at 8:10 am. Will you be on time for school at 8:30 am?

Over to you!

h

Topsy-turvy tip

How many minutes does it take to cover each of the three parts of the road?

TEXAS COMES TO THE EIFFEL TOWER

A tourist bus from Texas stops in front of the Eiffel Tower. One third of the tourists use the stairs to climb up and stop at the first floor to eat at the restaurant. All the others take the lift, but a quarter of them stop at the second floor to write postcards. The last 24 go all the way up to the third and last floor. Some time later, they all get back on the bus, except for one tourist who breaks his foot coming down the stairs. How many tourists meet in the bus?

Over to you!

Topsy-turvy tip

Does drawing pictures help?

60

TEACHING ENGLISH TO THE FRENCH

I am a student at the Collège Sainte-Blandine in Paris. We all have a detestable French accent in English. So our class is being sent to spend a month with some English families. Half of us will go to Portsmouth. Half of those remaining, minus one, will go to Winchester. And the last 7 are going to Cambridge. How many students are there in our class?

Over to you!

Topsy-turvy tip

Draw a diagram.

FIVE TAPS FOR ME AND TWO FOR BABY

If 5 taps can fill my bath with 50 litres of water in 5 minutes, 2 taps could fill my baby's bath with 20 litres of water in 2 minutes, right?

Over to you!

Topsy-turvy tip

How much water would one tap produce per minute?

A PINEAPPLE FROM THE IVORY COAST

I have 3 fruits in my fruit bowl: a 60 gram kiwi, a 110 gram banana and a pineapple from the Ivory Coast. The average weight of these 3 fruits is 390 grams. How much does the pineapple from the Ivory Coast weigh?

Over to you!

Topsy-turvy tip

What is the total weight of the 3 fruits?

DEAR PARENTS

"Dear parents,

We're very happy visiting Paris, it's just fantastic. Yesterday we saw Louis XIV's castle at *Wfstbjmmft*. Today we will visit the beautiful building where Napoléon is buried, the *Sedilavni*. Tomorrow we'll go up the tall and famous *Sntq Dheedk*.

Love from your daughters, Elise, Eleonore and Emily"

Try to figure out the 3 secret codes used here and decode the real names of Louis XIV's castle, the place where Napoléon is buried and that famous monument where you have to climb up high.

Over to you!

Topsy-turvy tip

Get out your Paris guidebook, then try to swap W for V ...

DINOSAUR STORY

Papa Dinosaur weighs as much as Maman Dinosaur with three baby dinosaurs. Seven dinosaur children and two baby dinosaurs weigh as much as Papa Dinosaur. How many dinosaur children equal the weight of Maman Dinosaur with one baby dinosaur?

Over to you!

Topsy-turvy tip

Subtraction is the clue!

CAROLINE, PAUL, FLORENCE AND BÉATRICE

If you have read the title of this problem, you now know the first names of my four children. I will also tell you that the average age of my three daughters, Caroline, Florence and Béatrice, is 11, while the average age of all my 4 children is 10. How old is Paul?

Over to you!

MY WONDERFUL LIFE

I have a wonderful life. I love sitting down to a meal and never miss one, be it breakfast, lunch, afternoon tea or dinner. Since the age of 18 months, I have enjoyed 100 000 meals! I want to celebrate this accomplishment on my next birthday. How many candles will I have on my birthday cake?

Over to you!

THREE KINGS

Jérôme, Louis and Joseph Bonaparte were Napoléon's three brothers. One was appointed King of Spain, another King of Holland, and the third brother became King of Westphalia. But Jérôme was not the King of Holland, the King of Holland was not called Joseph, and Joseph was not the King of Westphalia. Which country was ruled by Louis?

Over to you!

Topsy-turvy tip

Try to use sudokulogic with three rows and three columns. Or look it up in a good history book!

TROIS ROIS

Jérôme, Louis et Joseph Bonaparte étaient tous trois frères de Napoléon. L'un a été nommé roi d'Espagne, un autre roi de Hollande et le troisième roi de Westphalie. Mais Jérôme n'était pas roi de Hollande, le roi de Hollande ne s'appelait pas Joseph, et Joseph n'était pas roi de Westphalie. De quel pays Louis était-il le roi?

C'est à toi!

FRANCE-CANADA

France has an area of 550 000 000 000 m². Canada has an area of 9 900 000 km². How many Frances are needed to cover Canada?

Over to you!

Topsy-turvy tip

How many square metres in a square kilometre?

PARISIAN MÉTRO

We needed 12 Métro tickets, some full fare and some half fare. I had a total of € 20. One full-fare ticket costs € 1,50. A half-fare ticket costs half, of course. I bought 3 full-fare tickets more than half-fare tickets. Is this possible ?

Over to you!

Topsy-turvy tip

Watch out! if you add an even number to an odd number, the sum will always be an odd number.

SCOOTERS EVERYWHERE

There are twice as many boys as girls in our class. For Christmas, one girl out of three and one boy out of two received the most fashionable present: a scooter. On the first day back at school, 12 of us were on scooters. How many children do you think were, sadly, not riding scooters?

Over to you!

Topsy-turvy tip

Don't forget that half
the number of boys equals
the number of girls.

ANIMAL ROUND

A whale weighs as much as 3 elephants or 5 hippopotami.
A hippopotamus weighs as much as a rhinoceros or 2 giraffes.
A giraffe weighs as much as 4 zebras or 13 monkeys. How many
monkeys weigh as much as one whale?

Over to you!

Topsy-turvy tip

Watch out for useless
information!

LA RONDE DES ANIMAUX

Une baleine pèse autant que 3 éléphants ou que 5 hippopotames.
Un hippopotame pèse autant qu'un rhinocéros ou que 2 girafes.
Une girafe pèse autant que 4 zèbres ou que 13 singes. Combien
faut-il alors de singes pour égaler le poids d'une baleine?

C'est à toi!

RICHER OR POORER?

"You're doing a great job," my boss said. "I'm giving you a 10% pay rise."

"You're getting rich," said my tax man. "I'm going to raise your tax from 20% to 30%."

Will I be richer, poorer or the same as before?

Over to you!

Topsy-turvy tip

If I earn € 100 today, how much will I still have after I pay my taxes?

MY COUSIN'S DUCKS

My country cousin keeps ducks and a fine white goose. She has a Rouen duck weighing 3.3 kg and a Rouen drake weighing 4.5 kg. The other two ducks are from Brittany, and they each weigh 3.1 kg. The average weight of all her birds is 4 kg. So what is the weight of the goose?

Over to you!

Topsy-turvy tip

What is the total weight of the birds?

TARTE TATIN

We just love desserts in my family, especially ones made with fruit. On my brother Pascal's birthday, Maman made a Tarte Tatin, a yummy apple tart, which weighed 540 grams. Pascal and our cousins Jean-Jacques and Victor each took $\frac{1}{6}$, adding much cream on the top. My twin sister and I each took $\frac{1}{4}$, without adding cream. How much Tarte Tatin was left for Papa when he came home from work?

Over to you!

RACING TO THE TOP OF THE EIFFEL TOWER

The Eiffel Tower is 300 metres high. Yvette climbs 1 metre up the stairs on foot every 10 seconds, but Monique decides to take the lift. She has to queue up for 23 minutes, then spends 6 minutes in the first lift, queues for another 12 minutes on the second floor and spends 4 minutes in the second lift to get to the top. Who reaches the top first?

Over to you!

ADVENTURE ON
THE CHAMPS ELYSÉES

It is 4:41 pm. Here you are at the Place de la Concorde at the eastern end of the Champs Elysées. You have € 29 in your purse. You stroll down the Champs Elysées for 13 minutes and then decide to go and see a film that lasts 1 hour and 53 minutes. Then you walk another 13 minutes and arrive at the Arc de Triomphe at the other end of the Champs Elysées. Suddenly, a pickpocket steals your purse. You go to the police station and tell them that the number of euros stolen is equal to the time in hours that the theft took place. How much was your ticket at the cinema?

Over to you!

Topsy-turvy tip

At what time did you reach the Arc de Triomphe?

SOLUTIONS
EASY

BON APPÉTIT TO THE LIONS P6

4 lions eat 4 gazelles in 4 days. Imagine each lion with its own gazelle: that is, 1 lion eats 1 gazelle in 4 days. So 2 lions eat 2 gazelles in 4 days.

CHRISTMAS LOG P6

No, she doesn't. 1 cut takes 2 seconds. To cut it into 5 slices takes 4 cuts, or 8 seconds.

HOW OLD IS GRAND-PÈRE? P7

Maman's age (38) plus 31 makes 69 years.

FAST FOOD P8

One hamburger and one portion of chips cost € 4. So two hamburgers and two portions of chips cost € 8. Two hamburgers and two portions of chips with orange juice cost € 9. So the juice costs € 1.

MAMAN, MY TWIN SISTER AND ME P8

Last year, Maman was 36 and I was 9. This year, my twin and I are 10.

MÉTRO OPÉRA P9

$\square - 9 + 13 = 57$
$\square + 4 = 57$
$57 - 4 = 53$ people

A FRAGRANT DINNER P10

3 cauliflowers at € 2 → € 6
15 cm of garlic sausage at € 0,15 → € 2,25
Half a Camembert at € 5 each → € 2,5
A kilogram of turnips at € 1 per half-kilo → € 2
A jar of bouillabaisse → € 6
Total: € 18,75
€ 20 − € 18,75 = € 1,25
Yes, I have € 1,25 left over.

TARZAN IN HONOLULU P10

Tarzan screamed at 6:30 pm, 6:23 pm, 6:16 pm, 6:09 pm, 6:02 pm, 5:55 pm, 5:48 pm, 5:41 pm, 5:34 pm, 5:27 pm and 5:20 pm – that's 11 screams.

ABDULLAH IN THE DESERT P11

34 legs − 2 (Abdullah's) = 32 legs
32 ÷ 4 = 8 animals
8 animals with 13 humps is 5 camels (2 humps each) and 3 dromedaries (1 hump each), so there are more camels than dromedaries.

QUICHE LORRAINE P12

The diameter of the pan, 32 cm, is greater than the depth of the oven, 31 cm. So the quiche will not fit in the oven.

ADORABLE TRIANGLES P12

    equilateral triangle

    isosceles triangle

    right-angled isosceles triangle

    ruined triangle

    right-angled triangle

AT THE BAKER'S P13

2 croissants and 4 pains au chocolat cost € 5,40.

Halve everything: 1 croissant and 2 pains au chocolat cost € 2,70.

Multiply it all by 3. Three croissants and 6 pains au chocolat cost € 2,70 × 3.

€ 2,70 × 3 = € 8,10

WAGADA KOKONIMOON P14

octopus	530 g
11 crabs	1399.2 g
sea tortoise	4070 g

Total: 5999.2 g or 5.9992 kg
Wagada will not starve!

TEN KILOMETRES OF HAIR P14

Gargantua's total hair is 10 km or 10 000 m.
One hair is 4 cm, so 25 hairs are 100 cm
or 1 m.
25 000 hairs are 1000 m or 1 km.
250 000 hairs are 10 000 m or 10 km.
So Gargantua has 250 000 hairs.

WITH PAUL AT CHIWAKATEPEC P15

The group climbs at 100 metres per hour →
600 metres in 6 hours (arrive 1 pm)
Paul climbs 2 metres per minute → 120
metres an hour → 600 metres in 5 hours
(arrives 12 noon)
We can have lunch at 1 pm.

CHOCOLATES FOR EASTER P16

4 chocolate hens and 3 chocolate bells cost
€ 13,10.
3 chocolate hens and 2 chocolate bells cost
€ 9,40.
Subtract one sum from the other to get the
cost of 1 chocolate hen and 1 chocolate bell:
€ 13,10 − € 9,40 = € 3,70

UP THE EIFFEL TOWER P16

- 9 m Marion
- 8 m Lucile
- 4 m Emilie
- 2 m Violette
- 0 m myself

I am the one who has to buy ice cream for
the other four!

MAMAN IS A MATHS TEACHER P17

Anne-Sophie only made 2 mistakes, so she
will get the better mark.

MATHS TEST P17

I lasted 3197 seconds (52 × 60 plus 77),
Violette 3213 seconds and Pierre-Alexandre
3180 (53 × 60). Pierre-Alexandre gave up first.

A MYSTERY P18

08 and 19 both have 8 more units than tens.
But 08 does not really make sense. Result: 19

300 METRES OF EIFFEL TOWER P18

Gustave Eiffel was born on 15 December 1832.
The foundations were started in late January
1887. The tower was completed at the end
of March 1889, 2 years and 2 months later.
Construction lasted 26 months.

BAKED EGGS P19

In 3 days, you get 7 eggs. To get 14 eggs,
you need 6 days.

SEVEN CRAZY ARROWS P20

The only arrow that has no lost its mind is
the one pointing to the word 'ellipse'.

A KHAKI ANORAK P21

The anorak was on sale with a 50% (or $\frac{1}{2}$)
discount, so € 40 is $\frac{1}{2}$ of the original price.
The original price is € 80.

ANOTHER SEVEN CRAZY ARROWS P22

The only arrow that has not lost its mind is
the one pointing to the word 'reflex angle'.

TAKE CARE OF YOUR TEETH P23

4 children eat 4 bags of sweets in 4 days.
Imagine each child with its own bag: that is,
1 child eats 1 bag in 4 days. So 10 children eat
10 bags in 4 days.

MIRROR, MIRROR ... P23

I have 2 stripes on my sweater.

THE LITTLE WATER LILY AND THE BIG CASTLE P24

Work backwards:
After 20 days, the entire pond was covered.
After 19 days, half the pond was covered. After
18 days, a quarter of the pond was covered.

PARIS-LONDON-HELSINKI P25

Helsinki is 2 hours ahead of London, so the answer is 2:30 pm.

SMALL TOYS P25

A cowboy costs € 1.

A farmer costs as much as 5 cowboys: that is, € 5.

A farmer costs € 3 more than a Gaul, so a Gaul costs € 2.

A Roman soldier costs the same as a Gaul: that is, € 2.

Napoléon on horseback costs € 2 more than a Roman soldier: that is, € 4.

SUDOKULOGIC P26

			Total
0	0	1	1
1	0	0	1
0	1	0	1
Total 1	1	1	

EVERYTHING EVERYWHERE P27

The information is printed in below with 0s to show no correspondence between the rows and columns.

On the basis that there is one thing in each house (and thus a 1 in each row and each column), the maths notebook is at Grand-Mère and Grand-Père's house.

	Maman	Papa	Grand-Mère/ Grand-Père's
maths notebook	0	0	1
sports kit	1	0	0
pencil case	0	1	0

MOTHER'S DAY P27

3 roses, 2 tulips and 3 marguerites cost $3 + 1 + 1 = € 5$.

So I don't have enough for an extra tulip.

MEDIUM

PARIS-BIARRITZ P28

With 42 litres, you can drive 7 times 100 km, or 700 km. To drive 800 km, you will need to refill your tank.

IN THE BELLY OF THE WHALE P28

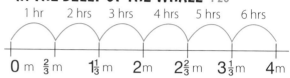

Jonah covers 2 metres in 3 hours. To cover 4 metres, he will need twice as long or 6 hours.

THE SNAIL AND THE TORTOISE P29

The tortoise moves 300 cm in 180 minutes.

The snail moves 2 cm in one minute or $2 \times 180 = 360$ cm in one minute. The snail is the winner.

GOING TO SCHOOL P30

Alice's house   Colombe's house   and Jeanne's house

For Alice's house, there are 4 intersection points where an odd number of lines is attached (it is impossible to draw the house in a single line). This is also true for Colombe's house. For Jeanne's house, there are only 2 odd points. Choose one of these points to start your drawing and the other to finish it.

HOW OLD IS PAPA? P30

When Papa was 8, Grand-Père was 39. Eight years before, when Papa was 0, Grand-Père was 31. When Papa is 31, Grand-Père is 62, twice as old as Papa. So Papa is 31 years old.

FROM MARSEILLES TO NEWCASTLE P31

Number of beds:

$(140 \times 2) + (156 \times 4) = 280 + 624 = 904$

Number of people in the cars:

$(180 \times 3) + (180 \times 2) = 180 \times 5 = 900$

Four beds will then be empty.

FRENCH HISTORY P32

Louis XVIII: 1815 to 1824 (9 years)

Charles X: 1824 to 1830 (6 years)

Louis-Philippe: 1830 to 1848 (18 years)

République: 1848 to 1852 (4 years)

Napoléon III arrives in 1852.

ANATOLE AND ZOÉ P32

There are 4 boys and 3 girls in this family.

MINIATURE CARS P33

The information is printed in bold type below. The 0s indicate that there is no correspondence between the lines and columns.

	Peugeot	Citroën	Renault
grey	**1**	0	0
black	0	**1**	0
red	0	0	**1**

The Citroën is black.

AERIAL VIEWS P34

Maman's house   Papa's house

Area: 49 square metres   Area: 48 square metres

Perimeter: 28 metres   Perimeter: 32 metres

I spend Christmas with Papa and Easter with Maman.

FISH WITH RASPBERRIES P34

No, because she already has 10 packets.

POLYTECHNICIANS' PARADE P35

Number of students per line:

$2 + 1 + 17 = 20$

Number of students per column:

$21 + 1 + 8 = 30$

Total number of students at the Polytechnique: $20 \times 30 = 600$

THE DELAROCHE-DUPLESSIS FAMILY P36

The children could be aged:

0, 2, 4, 6, 8

1, 3, 5, 7, 9

2, 4, 6, 8, 10

3, 5, 7, 9, 11

and so on

The last set of numbers would give 35 candles, so Augustin-Charles must be 11.

EVERYBODY INTO THE CAR P36

$85 + 65 + 18 + 42 + 27 + \text{me} =$

237 kilos + me = 264 kilos

1587 − 1323 kilos

I weigh: 264 − 237 kilos = 27 kilos

AN ELEPHANT FOR THE WHOLE CLASS P37

If all the students were girls, the total weight would be $28 \times 33 = 924$ kilos (less than Robrouf's weight). Because some are boys, the total weight is even less. So, naturally, Robrouf weighs more than all the students together.

AT THE CHÂTEAU DE SAILLESVER P38

One pound was worth 11 francs, and a ticket cost 33 francs.

Former price: $33 \div 11 = £3$

Today, one pound is worth € 1,5, and a ticket costs € 3.

New price: $3 \div 1.5 = £2$

The new price is cheaper.

PARIS BLUES P38

The information is printed in bold type below. The 0s indicate that there is no connection between the line and column.

	Django Lejeune	Joe Tatin	Charlie Lepetit
percussion	0	**1**	0
piano	0	0	**1**
trumpet	**1**	0	0

Charlie Lepetit plays the piano.

FROM 1 TO 99 P39

In the first decade (1 to 10), the tens position does not show zeros. Therefore, 0 is the numeral used the least.

I LOVE EURO DISNEY! P39

	nausea	nightmares	headache
Pirate Ship	1	**0**	**0**
Ghost Mansion	0	0	1
Magic Mountain	**0**	1	**0**
	1	1	1

The nightmares were due to the Magic Mountain.

WATERLOO STATION P40

$1815 + 33 + 150 = 1998$
We have already celebrated its birthday.

THE DUBOIS FAMILY P40

Last year, Marie was 5.
This year, she is 6, and the others are 9, 12, 15, 18 and 21.
Their ages total 81, so 80 candles will not be enough.

ALEXANDRINE IN PARIS P41

There are four land areas:
Right Bank (7 bridges)
Île de la Cité (10 bridges)
Île Saint-Louis (6 bridges)
Left Bank (7 bridges)
Two areas are linked by an odd number of bridges. Start from one of the two land areas (the Right Bank, for example) to reach the other (the Left Bank). You can check this during your next trip to Paris!

MY GREAT-GRANDMOTHER'S 100TH BIRTHDAY P42

Two years ago, my great-grandmother was $93 + 3 = 96$ years old. She is now 98. She will celebrate her 100th birthday in 2 years.

FEEDING THE GIRAFFES P42

1 giraffe eats 3 boxes in 2 days.
2 giraffes eat 3 boxes in only 1 day.

2 giraffes eat 3×3 boxes in 3 days.
$3 \times 3 = 9$ boxes

STEAK FRITES FOR MARGUERITE P43

$$\frac{20}{4} + \frac{8}{2} - \frac{15}{5} + \frac{6}{3} - \frac{7}{7} =$$
$$5 + 4 - 3 + 2 - 1 = 7$$
As Marguerite only has 7 teeth, you can't feed her a steak dinner.

THE TRUE STORY OF NOAH'S ARK P44

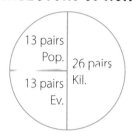

Number of pairs on Popocatepetl: 13
Number of pairs on Mount Everest: 13
Number of pairs on Kilimanjaro: 26
Total number of pairs: 52
Total of animals saved: $52 + 2 = 104$

AUSTERLITZ STATION P44

$1802 + 63 + 150 = 2015$
Parisians will celebrate the anniversary in 2015.

TRAVELLING P45

My blue suitcase and my green suitcase weigh the same. If the yellow suitcase weighed 3 kilos more, the total weight would be 30 kilos. The blue and green each weigh 10 kilos; the yellow suitcase weighs 7 kilos.

PAPAYAS AND KIWIS P46

Find the difference between the two purchases:
3 papayas 1 mango   2 kiwis ➞ € 9,25
2 papayas   1 kiwi ➞ € 5,50
1 papaya   1 mango   1 kiwi ➞
€ 9,25 − € 5,50 = € 3,75

ANNA, PHOEBE AND HARRIET GO TO PARIS P47

$50 \times 1,5$ ➞ € 75 to spend

Each girl spends 7,5 + 5 + 9,5 → € 22

Total: 3 × 22 = € 66

They only have € 9 left to spend.

SUDOKUSTATISTICS P48

			Total
	2	11	13
	6	2	8
	3	3	6
Total	11	16	27

JUDO FOR GIRLS AND DANCING FOR BOYS P49

	Girls	Boys	Total
Dance	11	2	13
Judo	2	6	8
Swimming	3	3	6
Total	11	16	27

Two girls have judo lessons, and two boys do dance – the numbers are the same.

PRINCESS KARAMAKAKIZOFF P49

Princess Karamakakizoff + husband →
2 people

Children: 3 daughters + 3 son-in-laws →
6 people

Grandchildren: each couple has 3 children →
9 people

These children's spouses → 9 people

Great-grandchildren: each couple has
3 children → 9 × 3 people → 27 people

Total: 2 + 6 + 9 + 9 + 27 = 53 people

Number of seats remaining: 77 − 53 = 24

There are 27 fiancés – too many! Better not invite them, too!

HARD

MADELEINES P50

Add the numbers and find the square root:

1 + 3 + 5 + 7 + 9 + 11 + 13 = 49

So the box must have 7 madeleines

on each side.

Or draw the madeleines as follows:

The box contained 7 madeleines on each side.

(You can see that the sum of consecutive odd numbers starting with 1 is a perfect square.)

COMPUTER GAMES P49

You can see from the grid that there are 4 vehicles that are beige and non-amphibian.

	Amphibian	Non-amphibian	Total
Beige	1	4	5
Green	3	5	8
Total	4	9	13

MOBILE PHONES P51

You can see from the grid that 6 boys do not have a mobile phone.

	Phone	No phone	Total
Boys	1	6	7
Girls	3	11	14
Total	4	17	21

LONG LIVE THE CONCORDE! P52

Remember: New York time is 6 hours earlier than Paris time.

Leave New York 10 pm (Paris time: 4 am)

Travel $3\frac{1}{2}$ hours → arrive 7:30 am Paris

ORANGES AND FRIENDS P52

The sum of any seven odd numbers is an odd number and will never equal 28. The problem is impossible to solve.

WHEN JULIETTE TURNS 15 ... P53

If Sylvain is 2, Juliette is 2 × 2 × 2 × 2 = 16. This is impossible since she is under 15. So Sylvain must be 1 year old, Baptiste 2, Clément 4 and Juliette 8. She will happily turn 15 in 7 years' time.

QUENTIN, MARJOLAINE AND COMPANY P54

The information is printed in bold type below. We can presume that all children had either Marjolaine or Quentin as a parent – and no children had neither as a parent, so the bottom right space on the grid is empty.

We can now deduce that Quentin and Marjolaine had 3 children together:

	Quentin's children	Another father's children	Total
Marjolaine's children	3	4	**7**
Another mother's children	2	0	2
Total	**5**	4	**9**

FRUIT SALAD P54

5 lemons + 1 grapefruit → 12 kiwis

5 kiwis + 2 lemons → 1 grapefruit

We know 1 grapefruit is the same weight as 5 kiwis + 2 lemons, so, in the first equation, replace the grapefruit with those other fruits.

5 lemons + 5 kiwis + 2 lemons → 12 kiwis

Simplify: 7 lemons + 5 kiwis → 12 kiwis

Therefore, 7 lemons → 7 kiwis

One lemon weighs the same as one kiwi.

DEAR DIAGONALS P55

sides	diagonals
3	0
4	2
5	5
6	9
7	14

The number of sides increases by 1, and the number of diagonals increases by 2, 3, 4, 5, and so on. So if I have 14 diagonals, I have 7 sides.

AT THE PIZZERIA P56

Convert the fractions so they can be subtracted:

Charles left half less one-third:
$\frac{1}{2} - \frac{1}{3} \rightarrow \frac{3}{6} - \frac{2}{6} \rightarrow \frac{1}{6}$

Robert left three-fifths minus half:
$\frac{3}{5} - \frac{1}{2} \rightarrow \frac{6}{10} - \frac{5}{10} \rightarrow \frac{1}{10}$

Yves left half minus two-eighths:
$\frac{1}{2} - \frac{2}{8} \rightarrow \frac{4}{8} - \frac{2}{8} \rightarrow \frac{2}{8} \rightarrow \frac{1}{2}$

Robert has the best appetite.

BIG BALL P57

You need 8 times the ball's diameter to encircle the box twice: $8 \times 40 = 320$ cm

To tie the bow, you will have $400 - 320 = 80$ cm.

GRAND-MÈRE'S JUST FINE P57

Grand-Mère's age is $\frac{313}{17} + \frac{663}{23} + \frac{758}{17} + \frac{211}{23}$.

Add fractions with the same denominator, then simplify:

$$\frac{313+758}{17} + \frac{663+211}{23} = \frac{1071}{17} + \frac{874}{23}$$
$$= 63 + 38$$
$$= 101$$

Grand-Mère is 101 years old.

MARTIAN TOES P58

A Martian has $\frac{3}{7} + \frac{11}{4} + \frac{11}{7} + \frac{13}{4}$ fingers on each hand.

$\frac{14}{7} + \frac{24}{4} \rightarrow 2 + 6 \rightarrow 8$ fingers per hand and 24 fingers in total

A Martian has $\frac{2}{7} + \frac{5}{4} + \frac{5}{7} + \frac{7}{4}$ toes on each foot.

$\frac{7}{7} + \frac{12}{4} \rightarrow 1 + 3 \rightarrow 4$ toes per foot, which makes 28 toes in total.

Martians have more toes than fingers.

ABC P58

A, the 50° angle, could be the one 'on its own', as in Diagram 1, or one of the pair, as in Diagram 2. But angle B is neither 50° nor 80°, so Diagram 2 can't be correct. Angle B must be 65°.

GETTING TO SCHOOL ON TIME P59

You live 3 kilometres from school.

For 1 km, you do 5 km/h (1 km takes $60 \div 5$ mins or 12 mins).

For 1 km, you do 15 km/h (1 km takes $60 \div 15$ mins or 4 mins).

For 1 km, you do 20 km/h (1 km takes $60 \div 20$ mins or 3 mins).

The journey time is 19 minutes, and you arrive in time for school.

TEXAS COMES TO THE EIFFEL TOWER P60

$\frac{1}{3}$ stop at the first floor, and $\frac{2}{3}$ go on. Then a quarter of these (that is, $\frac{1}{6}$ of the whole lot) stop to write postcards, and $\frac{1}{2}$ (that is, $\frac{3}{6}$) go all the way up. This $\frac{1}{2}$ consists of 24 tourists, so in total there are 48. But one breaks his foot, so 47 Texans get back on the bus.

TEACHING ENGLISH TO THE FRENCH P61

Suppose half of those remaining went to Winchester, including the 'minus one' person. Then only 6 would go to Cambridge and the same number to Winchester. 12 would stay in Portsmouth. There are 24 students in total.

FIVE TAPS FOR ME AND TWO FOR BABY P61

5 taps produce 50 litres of water in 5 minutes.

Imagine the 5 taps. Each one produces 10 litres of water in that time.

Two of them will produce 20 litres of water in that time, which is 5 minutes, not 2 minutes.

A PINEAPPLE FROM THE IVORY COAST P62

If the average weight is 390 g, their total weight is 390×3 g, or 1170 g.

60 gram + 110 gram + ? = 1170 g

The weight of the pineapple is:

1170 g $-$ 60 g $-$ 110 g $\rightarrow$ 1000 g $\rightarrow$ 1 kg

DEAR PARENTS P62

Louis XIV's castle is in *Wfstbjmmft*, or Versailles (the code uses the letter one place further on in the alphabet).

Napoleon is buried in the *Sedilavni*, or the Invalides (the code writes words back to front).

The tall and famous *Sntq Dheedk* is the Tour Eiffel, or Eiffel Tower (the code uses the letter one place in front in the alphabet).

DINOSAUR STORY P63

Imagine Maman + 3 babies balancing 7 children and 2 babies in some large scales. Subtract 2 babies from each side of the scale. Maman + 1 baby weigh the same as 7 children.

CAROLINE, PAUL, FLORENCE AND BÉATRICE P64

The average age of all 4 children is 10, so their total age is 40.

Caroline + Florence + Béatrice + Paul = 40

We know the combined age of Caroline + Florence + Béatrice is 33.

So Paul is $40 - 33 = 7$ years old.

MY WONDERFUL LIFE P64

4 meals a day is 1460 meals per year (1464 in a leap year, so even it out to about 1461 a year).

Approximate number of years of happiness: $100\,00 \div 1461$ or 68.45

Approximate age: $1.5 + 68.45 = 69.95$ years

I will soon be celebrating my 70th birthday!

THREE KINGS P65

The information is printed in bold type below.

	Jérôme	Joseph	Louis
Spain	0	1	0
Holland	**0**	**0**	1
Westphalia	1	**0**	0
Total	**1**	**1**	**1**

We can conclude that Louis was King of Holland.

FRANCE-CANADA P66

A square kilometre is the same as 1 000 000 square metres.

$1000 \, m = 1 \, km$

$1000 \, m = 1 \, km$

France has an area of 550 000 000 000 m² or 550 000 km².

You need 18 Frances (18 × 550 000 km² or 9 900 000 km²) to cover Canada.

PARISIAN MÉTRO P66

Ignore the money.

Half fare	0	1	2	3	4	5
Full fare	3	4	5	6	7	8
Total	3	5	7	9	11	13

When the number of half-fare tickets is even, the number of full-fare tickets is odd.

When the number of half-fare tickets is odd, the number of full-fare tickets is even.

This means that the total number of tickets is always odd (because O + E = O).

So it is impossible that we bought 12 Métro tickets as 12 is even.

SCOOTERS EVERYWHERE P67

One girl out of three got a scooter, so the number of girls must be a multiple of 3. One boy out of two got a scooter, so the number of boys must be a multiple of 2. There are twice as many boys as girls.

A chart of possible numbers shows:

Girls in class	Boys in class	Girls with scooters	Boys with scooters	Total scooters	Total children
(multiple of 3)	(multiple of 2)				
3	6	1	3	4	9
6	12	2	6	8	18
9	18	3	9	12	27

The total number of children in the class is 27. Subtract 12, so the number of scooterless children is 27 − 12 = 15.

ANIMAL ROUND P68

1 whale weighs as much as 5 hippopotami.

1 hippopotamus weighs as much as 2 giraffes.

1 giraffe weighs as much as 13 monkeys.

So one whale weighs as much as 5 × 2 × 13 = 130 monkeys.

RICHER OR POORER? P69

If I earn € 100, I will have € 80 after paying € 20 in taxes.

If I earn € 110, I will have € 77 after paying € 33 in taxes.

So I'll be poorer than I used to be. This is true whatever salary I start with.

MY COUSIN'S DUCKS P69

The 4 ducks weigh 3.3 kg + 4.5 kg + 3.1 kg + 3.1 kg = 14 kg.

If the average weight of all 5 birds is 4 kg, their total weight is 5 × 4 kg = 20 kg.

So the goose weighs the difference between 20 kg and 14 kg: 6 kg.

TARTE TATIN P70

$\frac{1}{6}$ of the tart → 90 grams

$\frac{1}{4}$ of the tart → 135 grams

Nothing is left for Papa!

RACING TO THE TOP OF THE EIFFEL TOWER P70

Yvette's time: 3000 sec = 50 min

Monique's time: 23 + 6 + 12 + 4 min = 45 min

Monique gets there first.

ADVENTURE ON THE CHAMPS ELYSÉES P71

Time of the theft: 4 hours 41 min + 13 min + 1 hour 53 min + 13 min = 7 pm

Price of the movie: € 29 − € 7 = € 22